How to use this book

Follow the advice, in italics, given for teachers on each page.
Praise *the children at every step!*

Detailed guidance is provided in the Read Write Inc. Phonics Handbook

8 reading activities

Children:
- *Practise reading the speed sounds.*
- *Read the green and red words for the story.*
- *Listen as you read the introduction.*
- *Discuss the vocabulary check with you.*
- *Read the story.*
- *Re-read the story and discuss the 'questions to talk about'.*
- *Re-read the story with fluency and expression.*
- *Practise reading the speed words.*

Speed sounds

Consonants   *Say the pure sounds (do not add 'uh').*

f	l (ll)	m	n	r	s	v	z (s)	sh	th	ng nk

b	c k ck	d	g	h	j	p	qu	t	w	x	y	ch

Vowels   *Say the sounds in and out of order.*

at	hen	in	on	up	day	see	high	blow	zoo

*Each box contains one sound but sometimes more than one grapheme. Focus graphemes are **circled**.*

Green words

Read in Fred Talk (sounds).

vet   leg   bad   rub   bit   sit   <u>th</u>is   cra<u>sh</u>   wi<u>ll</u>

his   is   li<u>ck</u>   wag

Read the root word first and then with the ending.

jump   →   jump<u>ing</u>

Red words

<u>the</u>   s<u>ai</u>d   I   of   my

Vocabulary check

Discuss the meaning (as used in the story) after the children have read the word.

definition:

vet   *an animal doctor*

Punctuation to note in this story:

Ben Ned	*Capital letters for names*
This My Sit	*Capital letters that start sentences*
.	*Full stop at the end of each sentence*
!	*Exclamation mark used to show anger*
...	*Wait and see*

My dog Ned

Introduction
Why do we go to a doctor?
When animals are ill, we take them to see a vet.

Ben has a big hairy dog called Ned. One day Ned starts to limp and feel very sorry for himself. Ben takes Ned to the vet. The vet rubs ointment on the leg and Ned sniffs it very suspiciously. Suddenly he starts to feel better and gives the vet a big surprise.

Story written by Gill Munton
Illustrated by Tim Archbold

This is Ben.

This is Ned.

Ned is Ben's dog.

Ned has a bad leg.

Yap yap

This is the vet.

"My dog has got a
bad leg," said Ben.

"Sit, Ned," said the vet.

Ned sat.

"I will rub a bit of this on his leg," said the vet.

Rub rub

Sniff sniff

"Get up, Ned," said the vet.

Ned got up.

Crash!

"Sit, Ned," said the vet.

"Sit!"

Wag wag

Lick lick

Questions to talk about

FIND IT QUESTIONS

✔ *Turn to the page*

✔ *Read the question to the children*

✔ *Find the answer*

Page 9:   *Why did Ben take Ned to the vet?*
How would you describe Ned when he had a bad leg?
(sorry for himself / angry / fed up / miserable)

Page 11:   *What did the vet do to help Ned?*

Page 13:   *What does Ned feel now?*
(excited / lively / joyful / bubbly / enthusiastic / grateful)